Children's Stories from the Qur

The Ark of Nuh علیه السلام and the Animals
COLOURING BOOK

SANIYASNAIN KHAN

COLOUR A STORY

Goodword**kidz**

Long, long ago, in the days of the Prophet Nuh (or Noah), people did not worship Allah. So Allah sent Nuh ﷺ to them with the message of truth. For a very long time, Nuh ﷺ tried to lead them to the right path, but only a very few poor people paid any heed. In fact, the rich people tried to harm Nuh ﷺ. So Nuh ﷺ prayed to Allah for help and Allah asked him to build an Ark, saying that to punish these bad people, he would send a great flood. So Nuh ﷺ, helped by a handful of believers, started building a huge Ark. People laughed at them.

When after lots and lots of hard and tiring work, the vessel was
ready to sail, Nuh عليه السلام asked all the believers to go on board in the
name of Allah. Allah told Nuh عليه السلام to bring along a male and a female
of every kind of living creature as well. Nuh عليه السلام had to keep enough
food to feed them all for a long time. This was a big job, but Nuh عليه السلام
and his followers carried it out with all sincerity.

One by one all the animals entered the Ark. Some had wings and some had legs; some crawled and some hopped. All came right into the Ark in pairs. The Ark became a huge barn for the animals and safe houseboat for the believers.

4

he animals came running—giraffes and rhinos, elephants and
amels, monkeys and wolves, cats and kangaroos, bears and horses,
ows and sheep, lions and tigers—and all went into the Ark in pairs.

There were chickens and ducks, flamingos and hawks, peacocks and pelicans, ostriches and hens—to name but a few.

Birds both tiny and big that flew high above the earth came along too. All were gathered in pairs and led on board.

Tortoises, snails and turtles came crawling along the ground. Then came frogs and grasshoppers who hopped right into the Ark. Rabbits too ran races—let's see who gets on board first! And finally came the crocodiles with their big jaws.

No sooner had all the creatures come on board and the supplies ha
been stowed away, than black clouds began to cover the sky. First,
there was a drizzle, then the rains came. More and more rain fell
each day. Day after day, rain and more rain. The whole world
seemed to be dark. It became darker and darker with strong wind:
blowing from every side and water rising in huge waves as far as
the eye could see.

Allah commanded the floodgates of heaven to open and the ground to crack open so that a fountain of water came shooting up. The rivers overflowed and water fell in torrents. The Ark rose and fell on waves as tall as mountains.

More and more water came till the valleys were filled, the trees were covered by the waters, the hills disappeared and the mountains themselves sank out of sight. The world was like an enormous sea—the only thing one could see was water everywhere. Far down below, all those who had paid no attention to the call of the Prophet Nuh عليه السلام and remained on land were drowned in the mighty flood.

With the rain hammering on the roof and a great wind that roared all around, the Ark went on sailing amidst the waves. The thunder rolled and the lightning flashed from the angry skies. Everyone on board was very frightened, but Nuh ﷺ kept praying to his Lord for His Mercy at this great moment of trial.

When the flood had reached its peak, Allah commanded the earth to swallow up its water and sky to hold back the rain. The water began to dry up. The rain had stopped! The clouds began to part.

As the level of the water began to go down, the mountain peaks began to rear up out of it. The Ark was caught by the peak of Mount Judi, in a land now known as Turkey, and rested upon it.

The Prophet Nuh عليه السلام and the believers who were with him thanked Allah for saving them from such a devastating flood. Everyone happily came out of the Ark. The animals were led to safety.

Nuh ﷺ prayed: "Lord, let my landing from this Ark be blessed, for you alone can make me land in safety."

In this way Allah made the flood and the Ark of Nuh عليه السلام a sign and warning for future generations.